TWISTED TALES

2022

WORDS OF WONDER

Edited By Roseanna Caswell

First published in Great Britain in 2022 by:

Young Writers
Remus House
Coltsfoot Drive
Peterborough
PE2 9BF
Telephone: 01733 890066
Website: www.youngwriters.co.uk

Printed and bound in the UK by BookPrintingUK
Website: www.bookprintinguk.com
YB0523N

FOREWORD

Welcome, Reader!

Are you ready to step into someone else's shoes and experience a new point of view?

For our latest competition *Twisted Tales*, we challenged secondary school students to write a story in just 100 words that shows us another side to the story. They could add a twist to an existing tale, show us a new perspective or simply write an original tale. They were given optional story starters and plot ideas for a spark of inspiration, and encouraged to consider the impact of narrative voice and theme.

The authors in this anthology have given us some unique new insights into tales we thought we knew, and written stories that are sure to surprise! The result is a thrilling and absorbing collection of stories written in a variety of styles, and it's a testament to the creativity of these young authors.

Here at Young Writers it's our aim to inspire the next generation and instill in them a love of creative writing, and what better way than to see their work in print? The imagination and skill within these pages are proof that we might just be achieving that aim! Congratulations to each of these fantastic authors.

CONTENTS

Eastbrook School, Dagenham

Mihaela Rizescu (11)	52
Glevenan Fernando (11)	53
Kian Davey (11)	54

Glen Urquhart High School, Inverness

Jack Ashton (12)	55
Matthew Watson (12)	56
Rowan Mackay (13)	57
Felicity Jones (12)	58
Struan Hood (13)	59
Rowan Brockie (12)	60
Ossian Ballance (12)	61
Brandon Garrison (13)	62
Cody Frame (13)	63
Daisy Ross (12)	64
Joshua Clark (13)	65
Sophie Power (13)	66
Daniel van Loon (13)	67
Hayley Ross (12)	68

Heart Of England School, Balsall Common

Charlotte Jackson-Baker (14)	69
Olivia Goddin (13)	70
Emilia Pazukha (12)	71
George Hall (12)	72
Aqsa Ahmed (13)	73

Kingsthorpe College, Northampton

Bella Verlander (13)	74
Amina Begum (12)	75
Shumaila Chowdhury (12)	76

Marden High School, North Shields

Evie Scott (12)	77
Jena Yare (12)	78

Annie Harrison (12)	79
Ollie Merrilees (12)	80
Aaron Richardson (12)	81
Katie Mcleod (12)	82
Samuel Ratcliffe (12)	83

Ormiston Sir Stanley Matthews Academy, Blurton

Alex Levey (14)	84
Olivia M (13)	85
Lola Whitfield (12)	86
Skye Dawson (14)	87
Paige Smith (12)	88
Sehar Hussain (12)	89
Daniel Ward (12)	90
Layla Kenny (12)	91
Rhys Bagnall (14)	92
Daniel Yates (12)	93
Chloe Walker (14)	94
Finley Barker-Green (14)	95
Warren Brown (12)	96
Georgia McNair (12)	97
Maleeha Mahmood (13)	98
Alfie Brannigan (12)	99
Jacob Taylor (14)	100
Joanna Dyer (14)	101
Alfie Loveday (14)	102
Ellie Fletcher (14)	103
Daniel Dixon (14)	104
Lee Stanier (14)	105
Sasha Crutchley (13)	106
Kaylub Slack (14)	107
Theodore Priest (14)	108
Luke Meir (13)	109
Lexi Allen (12)	110
Brooke Simpkin (14)	111
Olive McCarthy (13)	112
Kane Garvie (14)	113
Bradley Peake (14)	114
Morgan Quinn (12)	115
Chloe Dean (12)	116
Owen Jurkowski (14)	117
Aleeza Wahid (13)	118

The British School Of Tashkent, Uzbekistan

The Hemel Hempstead School, Hemel Hempstead

Thomas Mills High School, Framlingham

THE
STORIES

THE LAST PANTOMIME

Jack arrogantly pounded on the keys of his golden piano, that only occupied one corner of the large empty house he'd become a prisoner of. Blinded by the immensity of his wealth, he drove away those who stood by him during his struggle.

"News about your mother sire," the servant spoke fearfully.

"Yes," Jack said with overwhelming hope.

"I'm afraid she couldn't escape the giant's unforgiving grasp."

Jack collapsed in a flood of agonising tears. With a sudden longing for freedom, he entered the giant's cage, and let his fate be what connected him and his mother.

Stella Douglas (14)

I HATE MY JOB

Bending to collect her, my knees ached, feeling the solid concrete road underneath. She looked up at me, eyes wide, bright as the evening moon.
"I'm sorry," I whispered, scooping her in my arms. "I don't understand why they don't just stop their cars."
She was an innocent baby fawn, such a beautiful, tiny creature. I turned my head, glimpsing another pair of wide eyes staring from the safety of the bushes. Seeing the mum's sorrowful face, I said, "It's okay, I've got her now, she is safe." Tears filled my eyes.
I hate my job. I am Death...

Thea Monument (15)

THE GRINCH DOES IT

One day Santa's going through his list for the 107th time as he's having breakfast, then brushes his 8 reindeer. Afterwards, he gets his sledge and carries it into the barn. Next, he picks up his 8 reindeer, ties his sledge and the 8 reindeer together with iron chains, then says the magic word, "Please!"

He flies away... up... 2... 3... go!

But he forgot his list. Finally, he finds it in the engine. Sadly the Grinch kicks Santa off his sledge so the world misses Christmas and the presents. Santa will never be back. The holiday is called 'disappointment'.

Atholl Langdon (11)

PET-RIFIED

My sweet little puppy furiously sprung towards a lady whilst I was walking him on a fine summer day. I was perplexed. He then leaped towards me, trying to bite my face off. I could suddenly feel my heart filling up with a great deal of sorrow. I realised this had happened before several times. I'd no choice but to take my best friend to the pound. Bewildered, I sprinted to the vet. Threatening looks surrounded me from every direction. After ringing the doorbell, I suddenly woke up in front of my own house, ringing my doorbell. I'd been sleepwalking.

Jenessa Rajakaruna (14)

THE SIDE CHARACTER

She was perfect in the audience's eyes and I was a shadow made to play a part.
He looked at her, enraptured by her beauty. And she fell for him as if Eros had shot an arrow right through her heart.
Through every universe from Romeo and Juliet to Jack and Rose, they were always connected like entwined souls.
And in every story I'm just the side character.
As everyone stayed for her story I hope you stayed for mine, for her happily ever after was the genesis of my misery.

Laurissa Prasad

MY POINT OF VIEW

My plan was in motion, I had stolen the cash. I was on my way out of the crime scene but there were lots of chemicals around. Of course that's what you expect in a place of scientific work. And that's how I got my face, white as paper, with lips as bright as blood. I had fallen into the chemicals, it was like bleach burning my skin. And ever since then I've been known as the Joker. All because of my jealousy. Now I've learnt not to care if I get caught, I just smile and walk.

Jennah Mukesh (13)

BEAST VS BEAST

One day, a twelve-year-old boy and his mum go to the foggy park. The boy lets go of his mother's hand and he realises she is gone. The boy uses this chance to wander around as a demon and eat the vampires and humans in the park. He does this for thirty minutes until he comes across his mother crying on a bench. He decides to go back to his human body and comfort his mother. He later lives the rest of his life in the human body. They live happily ever after.

Ivan Moreno Brito E Silva (12)

THE BACK ROOMS

I don't know how much longer I can survive in this place. The mono yellow, the moist carpets, the fluorescent lights on max, humming and buzzing. I have fought off so many things. I don't think there is an exit. I'm out of supplies. I'm exhausted. I've been searching for hours. Wait! I think I see a door... There's more of this maze, but it's different. Broken. I think it saw me...

Thomas Howard

THE TROLL AND THE GRUFF GOATS

A fresh, mushroomy scent wafted from the troll's friendly abode, when the pounding of goat hooves came, disturbing the land's peaceful slumber. The troll, being a neighbourly soul, greeted these three guests.

"Hello!" the troll greeted cheerily, beckoning towards his homestead. "Care for a spot of supper, there's plenty!"

"Why that would be perfect," one goat hissed slyly.

The four huddled together under the troll's bridge. They gorged, not on the prided mushroom stew, but instead the stew's creator!

Subsequently, the land silenced: the flowers stopped waving, the birds stopped chirping, and the content humming from the troll's dwelling, ceased.

Alexander Vickers
Ashlawn School, Hillmorton

THE END OF PETER PAN...

"Mummy, that was amazing," Thomas chirped in excitement. "I loved the battle between Hook and Pan." Instantaneously, a man climbed onto the railing of the bridge. He removed his green blazer. He turned around at the edge. The man glanced around, seeing the small boy walking with his mother.

"Please world, don't be as cruel to him."

His feet shuffled backwards until cold concrete was no longer beneath his feet and he was free falling.

"Mummy look. It's Peter Pan. He's going to fly just like in the movies," Thomas claimed, as the man's body disappeared over the edge.

Emma Oswald

Ashlawn School, Hillmorton

HUMPTY'S GREAT FALL

At the chalk outline of the crime scene, what had once been a perfect fun-filled ovoid was now in pieces, shattered like the king's heart. Who else could provide such mirth? Who could crack such jokes? His comical shape and witty one-liners made him the king's favourite jester.

Who had bumped Humpty off? Surely identifying Humpty's last movements would be easy with his jingling bell hat and shoes! The king's prime suspects included: Gingerbread Man, as he thought he was humorous and catching him was impossible, Chicken Licken, as he was clearly tired of being questioned about who came first...

Aaron Morris (12)
Ashlawn School, Hillmorton

HUMPTY-DUMPTY REBORN

The doctor stepped back to survey his creation in the flickering yellow light. Sounds of dripping water were drowned out by the whirring of machinery, competing with screeches from the oval-shaped creature adorning the worktop in the middle of the room. Suddenly, the whirring stopped as an alarm blared above and the shrieking fizzled out as the creature arose. Cogs protruded from its silhouette, its skin a collage of eggshell and corrugated metal. A twisted grin tugged at the doctor's lips as he murmured, "I'm a genius..." And a genius he was. He had put Humpty-Dumpty together again.

Aidan Kilcullen (14)
Ashlawn School, Hillmorton

DESTINED TO FALL

A classic tale. A group of heroes. What could go wrong?
Apparently, quite a few things, as it were.
He observed quietly as the city he grew to love crumbled
into ashes before him, from his view on the nearby cliff.
A friend stood by him, ever curious he asked, "So how did all
this come about?"
The answer was simple, so simple it almost seemed pathetic.
It was quite insulting to the heroes but nevertheless, he
answered swiftly.
"They failed, as they're always destined to."
"It's quite sad, isn't it? One group fails and the world falls
apart."

William Brown (16)
Ashlawn School, Hillmorton

UNTANGLED

"What are you doing, darling?" Mother Gothel queried. Rapunzel flashed a gummy smile as she turned into the room.

"I gave myself a haircut, Mummy. Do you like it?" the little princess squealed with glee, branding a pair of steel scissors and a lop-sided fringe.

"No!" Gothel screamed as she dived onto the floor, cradling the hair in her rapidly ageing hands. Her skin turned ashen in front of Rapunzel's eyes. Then finally to dust.

The heiress of Corona was then brought up by Pascal and his chameleon family and returned to her rightful home.

Zoe Parker (14)
Ashlawn School, Hillmorton

WAITING FOR DINNER

Sitting in my grimy but lonely home, nothing to do, nothing to say, nothing to live for. My eyes wandered back and forth from the top of the bridge and back to the floor. No goats had come over that grubby bridge in years until...
Click! Clock! Click! Clock!
My ears were deceiving me. A herd of elephants was going to come over the bridge in a matter of seconds. My body sprung into action.
"Showtime!"
In a matter of seconds, I'd scrambled up the brown sloppy cliff and onto the damp, slippery bridge. I'd finally get my well-deserved dinner.

Annabelle Pearce (12)
Ashlawn School, Hillmorton

THE WITCH AND HER CANDY HOUSE

I'm exhausted. I'm building my house from the ground up... again! Yes, I come home and it's gone! Oh, the naughty children! They sneak up and gobble my house down. They lick the plant pots and nibble the door frame until they've eaten every crumb. Today is the last straw. If I get so much of a hint of a child, I'll nab 'em, cage 'em, cook 'em in a pie and gobble them down! I'm not going to let any insolent child ruin all my hard work! Wait... is that children's laughter I hear? It's dinner time. I'm hungry...

Emily Worthington (14)
Ashlawn School, Hillmorton

THE MONSTER UNDER THE BED

I'm simple, just like them. I was given a second chance. A chance to make children happy but they never are. They constantly ask their parents, "Can you check under the bed?" You see, my job is to bring good dreams to children. But when the light from a phone or torch is shone into my face, I'm blinded so I'm unable to help children sleep through the night. Instead, they are plagued with horrific nightmares. I have been misunderstood from the moment I tried to help. I wish I wasn't known as the monster under the bed.

Inari Paige (14)
Ashlawn School, Hillmorton

THE CHASE

Bang! The crackling noise of the twigs underneath me made my ears shriek in pain and a sparkling shiver ran through my spine. A horrible odour filled my nostrils. The towering trees covered my only source of light, as the moon was slowly gulped down by the threatening branches. I was running for my life. It was the only way to escape. My heart was pumping as fast as a speeding train. I was frightened and perturbed. Suddenly, I felt a strong surge of a heavy weight crash into me. Everything in my body became immobile. I was caught...

Satvik Sonti
Ashlawn School, Hillmorton

THEY WILL REGRET IT!

Just like that... he was dead. I went to scream. I remembered a week ago, before all this happened. Every morning without fail, he'd show up at my door, ready to walk to school. His toothy grin was like a sunbeam burning through the dark, depressing clouds. Now he was gone. Forever. His cold body touched my fingertips. It felt like death... like his soul was passing through me. He was never afraid of death. He was afraid of dying and not being remembered. But until I can be with him again, the person who did this will regret it.

Amber Butlin (13)
Ashlawn School, Hillmorton

THE MADDEST HATTER

It was a pleasantly mad morning. I waited for her. And she came. She always did, always has. Always the same questions. Same face and bow. Every day, I simply laugh until my voice runs dry, and drink my tea. I always drink my tea. Besides, I 'killed time' so tea and trinkets are all Time can provide for me and my withering soul. The Queen wants me dead and I feel the same. I killed her. That is what I did. I slipped her tea, and her body crumpled. I won. I was the Maddest Hatter, ruler of all.

Laila Beneké-Orr (13)
Ashlawn School, Hillmorton

THE PERILOUS DANGER OF THE WORLD

This was a dangerous idea. I started running away from the orange and scorching flames. I heard the sound of crackling flames as they grew higher and higher. They roared louder than the voice of a lion.

I knew this was getting too jeopardizing. I accelerated faster. I could still feel the spark of the inferno that burned on my skin. I tried to find an escape. As I was running, I could hear the sound of a bark groaning. It then snapped. I did not know if I made it but then I saw a flash of light...

Manav Laxmidas (13)
Ashlawn School, Hillmorton

THE GREATEST MOMENT OF MY LIFE

Today was simply grand! It was time for my greatest moment that was about to commence! I was really agitated about it because I might demolish my chance of becoming super wealthy.

I consciously combed my smooth hair. Here it was! My moment to shine like a star! I composed myself and calmly went onto the stage. Without a second thought, I took some deep breaths and began to sing. My stomach was full of butterflies as I sang.

At the end I witnessed my fans cheering, the crowd going crazy with exhilaration. Obviously, they adored it. I was ecstatic!

Zaynah Rashid (15)

Barnes Wallis Academy, Tattershall

POISON DIES WITH ITS TARGET

"You didn't swallow any?" I asked him.

His blue eyes darted towards me. Quivering with fear. "Y-you didn't swallow, right?"

Shivering and shaking with fear, I tried to avoid imagining the worst... I could see him gasping for air, his hands shaking. I grabbed his trembling hand. There was no way I was letting go of Peeta. I couldn't lose him too.

His legs were weakening. Collapsing in my arms wasn't enough. His raspy breathing, his sullen sighs convinced me I was going to lose him.

"Peeta! Don't leave. Don't..." I choked.

"You've won, Katniss."

His heart stopped beating.

Zoe Adebola (13)

Bradford Christian School, Bradford

THE BEAUTIFUL DUCKLING

I'm the most beautiful duckling in the world. My vibrant white feathers sparkle in the sun and my bright blue eyes glisten too. I'm so pretty that everyone is jealous of me. They look at me in awe and constantly tell me that I'm 'the prettiest thing ever!'

Apparently, according to some people, I'm also the most selfish duckling they've ever seen. Because I'm only young, I don't know what this means. I think it's a compliment, so when people ask me what my personality is like, I make sure to tell them that 'I'm very, very selfish'.

Sara Taylor (13)
Bradford Christian School, Bradford

THE TRUTH ABOUT THE BIG BAD WOLF (THAT NO ONE WILL BELIEVE)

Nobody knows the truth. Should I tell? What's the point? They won't believe me anyway. I didn't *mean* to scare her, I really didn't. It was all a terrible accident, really it was. Oh dear, now I'm in a fix. Why do I have to be a wolf instead of a fluffy rabbit? Little Red would've scooped me up and carried me gently to her grandmother's house, probably would've kept me as a pet. I'd be stroked lovingly instead of being cruelly hewn at by a woodman's axe. Fluffy rabbits don't scare anyone but wolves do... especially big bad wolves.

Bryony Aldridge (13)
Bradford Christian School, Bradford

THE WOLF AND THE TWO PIGS

The wolf set out on his normal stroll, wandering through the woods. Out of nowhere, the two pigs came out. They started blowing at the wolf. The wolf was terrified of the two pigs. The wolf ran but the pigs kept blowing at him.

The two pigs wondered what happened to their young brother, who'd gone missing. They thought the wolf ate him. Their ancestors had been known to hate wolves as the wolves blew their house away! The new generation of pigs got the power to huff, so they blew the wolf's house down and found the young pig.

Zach Horton (13)
Bradford Christian School, Bradford

PRIMROSE EVERDEEN

"Primrose Everdeen."

My heart pounded in my chest. Me? The chances are one in a thousand. My vision blurred and I felt sick. Near me, I saw Katniss fall and thought I might faint too. I glanced up, the sweat dripped off my face. I saw Effie Trinket in her hideous spring-green dress. She gave me an empathetic smile and beckoned for me to join her on the stage. I swallowed my fear and shakily walked up the wooden steps. The last thing I remembered before I passed out was Effie's high-pitched voice and a rush of sickness.

Seth Taylor (11)
Bradford Christian School, Bradford

ELSA AND ANNA

I have to tell you, I'm Elsa. This story is crazy so let's get started.

It was a snowy day and my powers got out of hand. I accidentally froze Anna which I feel very sorry for doing. We took Anna straight to the trolls. They said she had severe frostbite and pneumonia. Sadly, the next day, she passed away and the whole of Arandale was in mourning.

Everyone was so sad that their princess had passed away. Everyone was blaming it on me. I ran to my magic kingdom and that's where I found out about my secret power...

Eileena Flanagan-Smith (11)
Bradford Christian School, Bradford

NOBODY KNEW THE TRUTH ABOUT BRUCE WAYNE

Nobody knew the truth about Bruce Wayne. He killed his parents. He paid a thief to rob and kill them. He caused the death of his two loving parents for money. He knew that he would be the richest man on the planet, he would be a trillionaire. He decided to become a philanthropist to cover his tracks. But it gets worse. He'd been killing people to cover his tracks too. Ever wonder how Robin and Superman died? He killed them. This isn't coming from a random person, this is coming from his butler, Alfred. God have mercy on him.

Samuel Ekeledo (12)
Bradford Christian School, Bradford

THE FINAL CASE

I was in Egypt with Hazel, on a boat. Another murder case was solved for the Detective Society. I was excited. I'd solved it! We were announcing it to everyone in a meeting, but our murderer jumped off the boat and pulled me into the ocean along with her. I struggled for breath as she dunked me under but I knew how to swim so I survived. No one knows I'm alive except Lucy and Hazel. I work as a secret agent. Hazel might work as an agent with me. That was our last case together for the Detective Society.

Alana Ajit (12)
Bradford Christian School, Bradford

GINGER'S SECRET

"Don't hurt me," was the screechy sound chiming to my ears whilst shaking the fudge-coloured floor. The sugary sweetness of my gingerbread grotto didn't eliminate the bitterness in my mouth as I pondered how to hurt this meagre boy.

My mind overflowed with flashbacks - to prison, to escaping, to the sight of freedom being lost, to the tower's ghastly thorns blinding me.

"Please!" the brat continued, whimpering.

"Not when I'm winning," I muttered before slamming the oven door shut to leave skin cooking and bones baking with his loathsome twin's grief-filled yells echoing from her cage, filling me with delight.

Chrystalla Kitty Shakas-Taylor (14)

Christ The King Catholic Voluntary Academy, Arnold

THE VILLAIN

Two villagers moved across the earth, insignificant to this creature, mere ants. Yet... it hadn't had fun recently. It made up its mind to play. It swooped down, swift as a hawk. The creature started toying with them like a child with a car. They were thrown up into the air, then dropped. Between jaws which had opened beneath them...

A day after, the villagers watched Hero fly, scanning for enemies. There. A villain called Nefarius. Swooping down, Hero's strength defeated Nefarious. There was celebration in the village as Nefarious dropped - between Hero's jaws, which had opened beneath him...

Samuel Murphy (13)

Christ The King Catholic Voluntary Academy, Arnold

ACCOUNT OF HAROLD GODWINSON'S SCRIBE 1066-1080

Fourteen years ago, Harold Godwinson won the Battle of Hastings by standing steadfast in the face of the Normans. Today he has been standing steadfast against the frequent Welsh raids and attacks from mainland Europe. I have seen him develop in character, stance and experience. He has become the King Arthur of our time, let his reign be long and peaceful.

We go on campaign almost every year, so Harold has sought to destroy the Welsh threat by conquest. It has gone well, and we have conquered southern Wales for the Saxons as we advance on mountainous North Wales...

Raphael Sloan (13)

Christ The King Catholic Voluntary Academy, Arnold

THE RIDDLE IN THE TRUTH

Tom heard Mrs Cole's introduction of this... Dumbledore... and as he looked the man up and down he sensed an unusual air about him. He smiled at Tom. Warmly. Was he a doctor? Not any he had seen. Would he take him away? No... He knew what he had done was bad but surely no one needed to get involved? He was just a kid after all.
Tom hesitantly shook the man's hand and throughout the strange conversation that followed, he glared at him, showing his mistrust, forever keeping hidden the dark secrets he possessed. He wasn't the villain. Yet.

Taylor Richardson (13)
Christ The King Catholic Voluntary Academy, Arnold

THE EXHIBITION

Each day I return to that place... The place where I could immerse myself in a field of liberal thought. Where I could always unveil something new beneath the infinitely intricate works of delicate hands. Where colours run wild and lights swim past scattered voids, burning enthusiastically. Something about it tugged my heartstrings, pulling me to be there...
The town clock struck and I abruptly awoke, coming to the realisation I had sat here for hours. Looking below, I noticed a sign: *The Cosmos - an artwork flourishing with life.*

Sophia Emslie (14)
Christ The King Catholic Voluntary Academy, Arnold

BANG

Bang. Bang. Bang. Three shots go off. People are screaming and limbs are crashing against my face. *Bang, bang, bang.* I see blood and children, torn clothes and lost phones.
Who will be the hero this time? To save them, to save me?
Bang. Bang. Bang. The final shots go off and I'm finding it hard to breathe like someone has cut my oxygen off. My weight starts to shift and my body falls to the floor. My wounds drain my blood and at last, the gun slips from my hands and into the police's grasp.

Keira Tennick (13)
Christ The King Catholic Voluntary Academy, Arnold

MACBETH 2

Macbeth wakes up and takes his head from the top of the spear. He remembers everything and goes to MacDuff's castle. MacDuff doesn't recognise Macbeth due to the wounds and he also doesn't know what Macbeth wants. Macbeth talks in a new language and he ends his speech with "Death is what we live for." Macbeth kills him and puts his head above the same spear.

He hears church bells ringing as if it calling him to come back to the castle. He goes to the castle and his wife returns with the same bloody hands.

Abdelrahman Mohamed (12)

Christ The King Catholic Voluntary Academy, Arnold

TWISTED GUY FAWKES

There it was in the middle of London. A pile of rubble that used to be Parliament.

It all started when Guy Fawkes came up with a plan to blow up Parliament. He had got his crew together and everything was prepared. Then one of the rebels realised his brother-in-law was going to be in Parliament on the day but he didn't really like his brother-in-law.

Soon was the day they lit the match and *boom*, parliament exploded. Then they went to the Ox Inn.

Charlotte Kirk (12)
Christ The King Catholic Voluntary Academy, Arnold

THREE TERRIFIC PIGS

Under the bed, Ben and Holly lay still. Dangerously crying at the dark atmosphere from the death of their grandma. *Knock! Knock!* The big bad wolf put Grandma's nightie on. He answered the door. "Yo yo yo, Grandma!" the pigs said. The pigs banged into the wolf, knocking him into the fire. The pigs munched on the wolf. Ben and Holly escaped. The two children ran out of the door, still feeling guilty for their grandma's passing away. Rapidly, they ran into the woods, until the three pigs left. When they left, they knew they were safe.

Lili-Mai Cook-Parkes (13)
Colmers School, Rednal

THE QUEEN OF HEARTS...

When I was a little girl my mother always said to me that I would never fall in love, it was a stupid thing. "Promise me Catherine that you will never fall in love."
"I promise Mother, I won't fall in love."
And I kept that promise and every day I would run away from every boy I saw. I would only talk to girls then one day this boy called Jester approached me. I walked away quickly.
"You dropped your book."
I hesitated then I snatched it out of his hands. He was confused why I behaved like that.

Llewellyn Griffin (13)
Colmers School, Rednal

UKRAINE WAR

The leader of Russia, Vladimir Putin was a great man who tried to wipe the whole of another country named Ukraine out. They were not as strong as Russia so they almost got wiped out and that would have become history but then other countries started supporting Ukraine. Countries like USA, China, UK, Canada and others. They supplied bombs, guns and other equipment for war and essential supplies to ease the impact on the victims. Within a few months they started to counterattack.
Within a few weeks, they started taking over Russia...

Israel Olufemi (13)
Colmers School, Rednal

ALADDIN

As Aladdin slowly got up he started to lose his balance as he stared down at the pit of gold and luxury below him. Aladdin gulped as he jumped onto the next platform but he caught his foot, slipping onto a glowing ruby. Luckily he caught himself so close to a lamp. The ruby rolled towards Aboo giving satisfaction to his eyes. Aboo's thieving hands grabbed the ruby... An echoed roar was heard... causing the whole cave to shake and Aladdin to fall. Aboo watched and dropped the ruby, despair running through his body. What had he done?

Demi-Louise Rose (13)
Colmers School, Rednal

FORCED RETIREMENT

When I was shot on Air Force One, I thought I was going to die. I wholeheartedly believed that I would finally join Hunter in the afterlife. But what about little Alex? What have I done to his life? And, would my old mentor even want to see me again?

I don't like to think about death, despite killing being my overall profession. But that's all it truly is, my job. Don't ask questions.

Will I go to Heaven? Probably not. Will I go to Hell? Honestly, I just desperately want to retire. If only I could have a home.

Maisie Madden (14)
Colmers School, Rednal

THE GIANTS AND THE BEANSTALK

The gruesome giants had finally been waiting for this. They threw the oversized bean into the soil and then it happened. The soil below their size 569 feet split into two like a scar in the earth. And there it was. The beanstalk. It was digging into the ground like a jackhammer. They all did what most people would, they climbed down the beast of a stalk. After a treacherous hour and 46 minutes, they were at the bottom. Confused. Scared. All feelings the giants had never felt before. Were they in Heaven? Or could it be Hell?

Toby Hood (13)
Colmers School, Rednal

THE LAND OF NEVER

Peter Pan has just won another battle against Captain Hook. He is a true hero. Or is it so?
Every night a few more children arrive in Neverland against their will, they are chained tight together. I am one of his victims, my name is Wendy. I have just escaped from an abusive house with my fairy sister, Tinker Bell.
We are now prisoners once again, though I do not worry as I know my sea-sailing prince will come and save me.
We met one summer evening and now we're bound to be together for the rest of time.

Katie-May Patton (13)
Colmers School, Rednal

WHY ME?

I never had many friends growing up. People always turned their back on me whilst harsh words were getting passed through my ears. I longed to be like them, meandering the roads. Now look at me. I was always told to take the right path until it hit me, I would rule this selfless, wicked society. To never be caught, secretly that's what I thought. I never knew it would turn out this way. Fighting with my heart and soul. I begged to get out of this mess. I hope people will understand my story. Sadness and sorrow. Why me?

Bethel Manre (12)
Colmers School, Rednal

THE EVIL CYBORG DINOSAUR PIGEON

I never really belonged. I was born a dinosaur but then as I grew older I started to notice changes like wings, better eyesight. I just thought it was normal but no one else looked like this. One day I saw this rift open near me so I touched it and then there were tiny talking creatures who shot me and turned me cyborg and then I remember being back home. So now I'm waiting for this stupid, annoying rift to finally open again. Then as soon as it opens I will jump right through and attack all of them.

Harry Hayward (12)
Colmers School, Rednal

THE NEVER-ENDING PAIN

My plan was in motion but he just had to ruin it. It was working too and was so easy. The leader of Team A made everyone hate him so it was easy for people to want to kill him but the captain had to assign the killer. His own team and the worst part was that I was stuck again with people undermining my talent. I tried to block out the agony to explode but unfortunately I didn't, instead I screamed. The world stopped then suddenly I felt something, something I never felt before. I felt peace.

Idowu Ajala (13)
Colmers School, Rednal

HERO BUSINESS

One day, a superhero named Titan was casually doing his hero business, stopping crime, when he got a signal. He was in town. Who is he? you ask. Well, it was Cyborg (the number one villain) that killed my dad. I need to go kill him in honour of my dad.

I left my home at a young age to train so I could control my power to kill Cyborg for what he did to my dad. I flew over to his base but he had my weakness (kryptonite). Wait a minute, that's my dad... "Argh!" Then silence.

Jack Crowley (12)
Colmers School, Rednal

I AM NOT A MONSTER

So I'm out. What now? I know, I'll look for a friend. "Hi..."
People are scared of me. Why? Why can't I find a friend? Am
I a monster? No, I'm not a monster but yet people are
calling me a monster. All I want is a friend. Why won't
anyone be nice to me? Please someone, anyone, talk to me
please. All I want is a friend to talk to. To laugh with, but no
one will let me ask them to be my friend. Please just let me
help. I am not a monster. I am not.

Wendi-Leigh Quinlan (13)
Colmers School, Rednal

THE BEARS' REVENGE

Goldilocks was just arriving home when she saw a house with the door unlocked. Wrongly, she decided to enter and was pleasantly surprised when she saw three bowls of porridge. The first one she tried was too salty, the second too sugary. But the third one... Perfect! She had a few spoons then all of a sudden, a sucking noise erupted. A black hole appeared in the bowl and Goldilocks was pulled in. She had learnt a lesson - Never touch somebody else's items.

Netheesh Thilothaman (13)
Colmers School, Rednal

LITTLE RED RIDING HOOD TWIST

You all know Little Red Riding Hood's story, but do you know it like this...
She went to give her grandma cookies but she stopped for flowers. She met a wolf.
He beat her to her grandma's. When he arrived, Grandma was dead... The wolf was shocked so he hid her. He decided to dress like her so Little Red Riding hood wouldn't get sad. When Red arrived, she realised it was the wolf. She called the woodcutter. He killed the wolf before he could explain. Then he killed Little Red Riding Hood. The woodcutter was the murderer all along.

Mihaela Rizescu (11)
Eastbrook School, Dagenham

THE THREE PIGS AND THE WOLF

Everyone knows the story of the three pigs but what if it was something like this...

Not long ago, there was a wolf. Everyone stayed alert because they thought the wolf would eat them. Nobody knew that I just wanted a friend.

Not far from me, three pigs were building three houses. The first finished, then the second finished. The last one built a strong house but the brothers were annoying him so much that he left.

The wolf was walking the same way as the pig. The pig met the wolf and soon become friends.

Glevenan Fernando (11)
Eastbrook School, Dagenham

THE WOLF'S POINT OF VIEW

All I wanted was some bacon. I asked the three little pigs but they all said no. So you know what I did? I got a flamethrower and set their houses alight, just like they did to my tail.

When I got to the last house, I asked politely again. The third pig gave me some bacon while he was eating it. As he was cooking my bacon, I checked for some lettuce. All he had was meat. He was happy that I'd got rid of the other two because they weren't happy that he didn't eat veg.

Kian Davey (11)
Eastbrook School, Dagenham

AN UGLY TALE

"Ow-ow! Please s-stop! N-now!"
Her sisters left Cinderella bleeding on the floor. Her magical fairy godmother had deserted her. *Bang! Bang!* "Who could that be?" the two ugly sisters said.
There stood Prince Charming. "How wealthy are you?" he asked.
"We have millions!"
Bang! Bang! Cinderella strived to get out. She saw him and fell instantly in love. He didn't hear. "No one loves me." She killed herself like Juliet.
The prince who needed money married one of the uglies. They did not live happily ever after. They argued and shouted until he had her hung for lying about money.

Jack Ashton (12)
Glen Urquhart High School, Inverness

HARRY OTTER AND THE OTTER OF THE PHOENIX

Harry and Dudley were dashing under a log chased by dementorcas. Dudley was close to death but Harry saved him with the powerful white patronefish charm. *Whoosh! Gone!* He had no choice. Dumbldotter's army and all angry otters were ready to fight Voldemorca. All of Unfish's rules were shattered like ice sheets by the Measle twins. Crazy fireworks. All otters were free to swim away from school. The Otter of the Phoenix swam to the ministry. When they arrived they saw Voldemorca. Fierce! Wand ready, Dumbledotter and Voldemorca destroyed the ministry in the midst of the horrific earth-shattering showdown.

Matthew Watson (12)
Glen Urquhart High School, Inverness

THE LOCH NESS MONSTER

I was sitting at my desk goofily grinning about what I'd done. I was sick of everyone thinking I was crazy so I showed them completely crazy. *Bang!*
"What did you do? I just read the morning paper, what the hell is a Loch Ness monster?" my mother screeched as my jaw dropped to the floor. "How did you pull this off? You really are a nutter aren't you, Jimmy?"
"But Mum, I was breathtakingly bored!"
"How did you get it in the paper? You're as mad as a hatter, I ought to send you off!"
"I sent it anonymously!"

Rowan Mackay (13)
Glen Urquhart High School, Inverness

THE THREE LITTLE PIGS

Three little pigs decided to build very different types of houses, they were made of stone, sticks and a treehouse. The three little pigs were just enjoying their day. Suddenly they heard shouting coming from further in the forest. They rapidly rushed out of their houses and looked around frightened, trying to find out where the shouting was coming from. The loud noises of fire engines suddenly filled the air. The brave firefighters ran into the forest and put out the fire. Finally, the fire was put out and everyone was safe. Everyone was delighted that they were safe. Yay!

Felicity Jones (12)
Glen Urquhart High School, Inverness

THE OTHER SIDE OF FING!

I turn around gracefully in my spectacular lair, and, *boom!* I am snatched by Selfless Slimy Sock. He grabs me like a lion's prey and shakes me about vigorously as I gnaw his fingers, not letting go for dear life. Wow! This thing really wants me, probably because I'm so wonderful and amazing. He is dancing and prancing like a boy's 7th birthday party. When he thinks he is cherished, he realises he is on my significant other, Honkapotmus. As he bursts and starts attacking Selfless Slimy Sock he dashes and dances around the forest. Now he is gone.

Struan Hood (13)
Glen Urquhart High School, Inverness

RED

Once upon a time, there was a girl called Red, who was very adventurous. One day she went outside without telling anyone. While she was away her family didn't notice. Time was getting shorter for Red to get back, but then her granny realised she had disappeared, so she set out looking. What she found was teeth-grinding. Red's bag and shoes were lying on the ground.

Minutes later, Red's voice sounded in the distance. She was out of breath like she was being chased. The noise stopped. Was she gone? Would she return? Dead? Who would find sweet Red?

Rowan Brockie (12)
Glen Urquhart High School, Inverness

X-WINGS

The X-wings were approaching the Death Star, they were as fast as lightning. The rebels back at base sat eagerly waiting for sweet victory. The X-wings zoomed down the dark and creepy trench. As an X-wing was violently shot down, Luke started to focus more on his target, the extruded exhaust port but suddenly the dark Darth Vader appeared in his TIE Interceptor. Before he could react, deathly Darth Vader started speedily shooting at Luke. He tried to avoid it, but suddenly he got shot down. The rebels had lost. So in a few short minutes their base was destroyed.

Ossian Ballance (12)
Glen Urquhart High School, Inverness

THIEF

When Jafar stole the genie lamp, he used his first two wishes to become sultan and the most powerful sorcerer in the world. Agrabah lived in fear, waiting for his third and final wish. To stop the power-mad ruler, Aladdin and the deposed princess, Jasmine would unite the people of Agrabah in rebellion. But soon their fight for freedom threatened to tear the kingdom apart in a costly civil war. What happened next? A street rat became a leader. A princess became a revolutionary and readers will never look at the story of Aladdin in the same way ever again.

Brandon Garrison (13)
Glen Urquhart High School, Inverness

A VERY ORIGINAL STORY

Ben Gunn traversed through the forest as fast as a cheetah. He suddenly found bones shaped like an arrow. He presumed there was treasure nearby. Scurrying away at the soil; he desperately tried to find the treasure he'd looked for three years ago. He heard a noise... He squealed in happiness. He had finally found the treasure. He lifted the treasure with as much strength as he could produce out of his weedy arms and opened the chest. There was a gold glow shining upon his face. His smile overpowered his frown. How could he possibly take it home?

Cody Frame (13)
Glen Urquhart High School, Inverness

THE UGLY ONE

Once there was a girl who hated being called the ugly sister. She was always compared to her stepsister because everyone called her the beautiful one. All she wanted was to find her prince. When she found out her stepsister was asked to the ball and she wasn't she was as furious as a fire. *Urgh!* she thought.

She was shopping in the village for the ball as she was still going to go, just by herself. She couldn't find a fancy, elegant, sparkly, glamorous dress for the ball, until a man came in with the most beautiful dress...

Daisy Ross (12)
Glen Urquhart High School, Inverness

A QUIET PLACE

Bang! The monster silently blitzes through the field, ripping through the dense metal silo like it was a chainsaw. The horrific headstrong monster dashes through the long grass going for the petrified people in the van but feedback from a hearing aid causes powerful pain for the girl. She takes out her hearing aid to stop the torturous pain. The monster can now attack the van with no issue. The father taking his last stand lets out a scream of anguish, signalling to his daughter that he never stopped caring for her and, *snap!*

Joshua Clark (13)
Glen Urquhart High School, Inverness

JAYLA AND THE GIANT BEANSTALK

Boom! The giant stalk grew like wildfire. The girl was baffled so she climbed it, way, way over the clouds to a secret land. She didn't stop. She got to the top and heard a deep voice grumbling, "Who goes there?"

The girl didn't say a thing, she was more terrified than a mouse so she rapidly hid. The man behind the voice was an enormous giant. The giant stomped away and the girl went to check out the castle. She found a golden egg and stole it but dropped the treasure. It shattered into a million tiny pieces.

Sophie Power (13)

Glen Urquhart High School, Inverness

RIPPED TO SHREDS

Jaws was happy swimming in the ocean with the baby that he'd adopted. Two weeks later Jaws was killed. His baby grew bitter and enraged. Soon after, he hunted down the hunters and slaughtered them. *Boom! Pow! Wow!* After three minutes the ship had sunk down to the bottom of the ocean. For some reason, the shark was still feeling angry so he became a land shark and killed everybody in the whole world. By this time he was rife with rage. He grew larger and angrier and angrier until all of a sudden, he exploded.

Daniel van Loon (13)
Glen Urquhart High School, Inverness

CINDERELLA

My big blue carriage arrived. Running out I jumped in. It took 10 long boring minutes to get to the palace. Arriving I saw the massive posh palace. Slowly I strolled up to the tall white doors. It was as loud as a herd of elephants in there. I went to get drinks but it was getting closer to 00:00. I had to leave. Bursting out of the doors, I ran down the stairs when suddenly my shoe fell off. My expensive glass shoe. *Crash!* It was lost forever! Smashed! Useless! In a million pieces. My dream was gone forever!

Hayley Ross (12)
Glen Urquhart High School, Inverness

WHY I'M EVIL

They're blinded by the hoaxed light of self-proclaimed angels and wonder why I'm so cruel. Nefarious. Malevolent. A malignant Mad Hatter who stumbled into the Devil's grasp. Prevalent rumours of my train of thought derailing into the depths of Hell give some answers for the malice in my veins. Others believe I was forged in the shadows, tasked by demons to poison souls. Then there're the empathisers who speculate that phantoms of my past are haunting my future and this foreshadowed fate is no fault of my own. However, despite their theories, some of us are simply just born evil.

Charlotte Jackson-Baker (14)

Heart Of England School, Balsall Common

WHO AM I?

My head wasn't always twisted. My morbid ways of life may alarm you, or even haunt you in the most uncomfortable way, but as I said, it hasn't always been that way. My trauma seems to be its own story, or person for that matter. The howls of ghouls still echo in my mind, and for whatever reason I can't escape it. The gut feeling of dread and horror, butterflies rapidly flying around inside my stomach, somehow lingers within me, and makes my blood curdle to this day. Who am I? you may wonder. That's something you'll never know.

Olivia Goddin (13)
Heart Of England School, Balsall Common

THE MIRROR

"Mirror mirror on the wall, who's the fairest of them all?" As it finally showed her vain but beautiful face, she smiled. The queen turned her gaze on a patterned box like an owl eyeing its prey. There was a boar's heart inside. Except there wasn't. She thought about Snow White, the lovely girl whose looks exceeded the queen's. She was named after her pale skin. Watching a scarlet liquid pool beneath her feet, the woman thought that the name 'Snow White' just didn't suit the girl anymore.

Emilia Pazukha (12)
Heart Of England School, Balsall Common

CHOICES

He sat there. He was curled up in the beaten-up house with a glimpse of sunlight peeping over the mountain. A gush of wind ran past him and the lonely, downhearted man took a look over his shoulder and saw a portal hissing in the distance. Without a second thought, the man bounced up from his corner and sprinted over to the portal. He had made it. The man stared blankly at the gateway and began to have second thoughts. What felt like thousands of questions, the only real question was; is it too dangerous? He stepped in...

George Hall (12)
Heart Of England School, Balsall Common

THE UNTOLD

Every story has two sides and my side hasn't yet been told! Nobody knew the truth about me. I grew up as an orphan. I was believed to be the last of my kind. I had a heart as pure as gold. My home invaded and threatened I rose up to become its only protector. I was betrayed. My horns were stolen so, not thinking, I took the infant daughter of the thief who stole my home. I took away the only thing that kept their kingdom standing. This was assumed to be evil. I call this pure revenge.

Aqsa Ahmed (13)
Heart Of England School, Balsall Common

JUST A CATERPILLAR

Now the hungry caterpillar wasn't so hungry anymore - he wasn't a little caterpillar any more. He was a big fat caterpillar. He built a house called a cacoon around himself. Weeks passed and his head began to throb; other life seemed so far away. His racing heart echoed within the inescapable abyss that engulfed him. Alone, solitary, isolated, secluded, lingering in the never-ending darkness. The enclosing walls suffocating. Although these walls were not the thing stopping him, he believed it was instead because all the real walls were all inside his head. Besides, not everybody got to be a butterfly.

Bella Verlander (13)
Kingsthorpe College, Northampton

SNOW WHITE AND THE SEVEN DWARFS WITH A TWIST

Nobody knows the truth about me, they think I have the perfect life and the perfect future but have they thought about trauma? The bruises from long-ago nightmares when there was little hope. The light shone brightly and the thunder crashed from fault. Not only do I have to go through this but I have to cope with a woman who came to take the throne and ruined everything. The thing is: do they understand anguish? Do they think everything is perfect? Nothing lasts forever...

Amina Begum (12)
Kingsthorpe College, Northampton

WHY PICK SHREK?

I never belonged wherever I was. I was always the odd one out. I had no one. There was a time after my parents had passed away when it was deathly quiet for days. I walked and walked with no one. All I found were trees and grass, sun and moon. But that all changed. I met a strange green man: Shrek. From then I met what felt like a million people. I was happy and safe. But now, years on, Shrek has a new life. Does he need me? Did he ever need me? I still need a friend...

Shumaila Chowdhury (12)
Kingsthorpe College, Northampton

THE TRUE TALE OF OZ

Everyone remembers the tale about the Wizard of Oz and how Dorothy got home safely. Well, they lied. This tale does not have a happy ending.

Dorothy, when clicking her ruby heels together, didn't take her back home to Kansas, but to another dream. It was more believable than a world where scarecrows could talk. This world was corrupt. Once young Dorothy opened her eyes once more, her new friends and companions were gone forever. Just then, she snapped awake. There stood her friends of Oz who she stayed with happily. I might have lied... it is a happy ending.

Evie Scott (12)
Marden High School, North Shields

SMEAGLE/GOLLUM - THE LORD OF THE RINGS POV

I couldn't help it. This overwhelming feeling came over me when he pulled the shimmering golden ring out of the river. As soon as I saw it, I knew it would be mine and I would do anything to get it. I asked him to give the ring to me as a birthday present, but he angrily declined. My anger increased by the second until I tore the ring out of his palm and pushed him into the swirling, turbulent river, knowing that he couldn't swim. He drowned.

From that day on the ring was mine. "My love, my precious..."

Jena Yare (12)
Marden High School, North Shields

20 YEARS LATER...

The revenge we had been planning for 20 years was now in action. That young girl, who practically robbed our house, had now left her grand mansion. It was now our turn to rob her and see how she liked it.
We cautiously tiptoed around the lake to get to her house. Blessedly, the door had been left open. There stood a substantial jewellery stand. Pure gold brought everything to life and silver dazzled everywhere. We started snatching the jewellery and proudly put it on. We exited the house looking like shiny statues!

Annie Harrison (12)
Marden High School, North Shields

THE BIG INTELLIGENT WOLF

I was just making my way through the forest to find the three little pigs when someone noticed me.
He said, "Hey, aren't you the big bad wolf?"
I responded, "Yeah, that's me. Can I help you?"
He then said, "The question is, how can *I* help *you*? Your strategy is always blowing down houses and it always fails on brick houses. Why don't you just open the front door?"
Then I said, "Why haven't I thought of that before?"

Ollie Merrilees (12)
Marden High School, North Shields

THE TWISTED JUNGLE BOOK

Suddenly, I woke up in the middle of the jungle. I had no idea where I was. Abruptly, lots of animals started running towards me as fast as they could. In a panic, I started running for my life. They started getting closer and closer. My heart was racing the fastest it had ever done. I ran to a river. There was nowhere else for me to go. The animals were within metres of me. I gasped a deep breath and took a leap of faith into the water. The animals did not see me again.

Aaron Richardson (12)
Marden High School, North Shields

DESMOND'S DEVILISH DAY

"Haha!" echoed through Desmond's brain as he slept on his cotton bed. Faces of the bullies, who lied about him, swam across his mind's eye. *Bang!*

Desmond woke with a start. He left his bed and was shunted by angel after angel. He was an orphan in Malcanto, the land of angels. He had skin as red as the stop light and horns as pointy as a needle. That's why he was bullied but today that would change...

Katie Mcleod (12)
Marden High School, North Shields

RAMBO AS A PACIFIST

Rambo walked through the woods. He looked round after the blistering sound of a gunshot. He started to run. He didn't want to hurt anyone. He slowed down and continued walking. After another gunshot, he started sprinting. He crawled through the spiny bushes that scratched his skin but he had to continue to get to the party he was invited to. The urge to get there made him continue.

Samuel Ratcliffe (12)

Marden High School, North Shields

FRAMED

I sat broodily in my chair. Suddenly, all the windows shattered into one million pieces. My arch-nemesis, Iron, emerged.

"You should have just come in," I cried.

"Brayton," he said. "You're going to jail."

"What? Why?"

"You robbed Sky Museum."

Hmm, I wasn't expecting that. I'd committed a crime a few months ago but not that one.

"I'm innocent! There's no evidence!"

"You mean this?"

Iron pulled out a painting. Realisation dawned on me.

"You, you broke in and stole it!"

Iron smirked.

"Yep, who do you think the people will believe? Me, their beloved hero or you?"

Alex Levey (14)
Ormiston Sir Stanley Matthews Academy, Blurton

BEAUTY AND THE BEAST AS NEVER BEFORE

Beauty and the beast is a perfect love story but have you heard the truth?

Belle walked out of the dance sobbing, "Nobody will ever love me!"

As she walked through the forest, a voice said, "You okay, love?"

Slowly, the princess looked around. "Who was that?" she asked desperately.

Unaware the princess had a weapon, the beast made himself known.

"Stay back!"

He went closer.

"You're beautiful."

"I said stay back!"

She slit him with her weapon.

"Take one more step and I'll chop off your head," she said angrily.

"Go on then," he said thinking she was joking...

Olivia M (13)

Ormiston Sir Stanley Matthews Academy, Blurton

ADAM VERSUS THE BEAST

"Good morning Chip," whispered Belle.

"Good morning Belle."

She carried on speedily cleaning. *Knock! Knock!* She strode to the door.

"Oh, hello Mother and Father."

They stood still.

"We have a surprise..."

They stepped aside and Adam appeared. He was the same age as Belle. He looked smart and posh.

"Hello, Belle," he said in a posh voice.

To cut a long story short, he wanted to marry Belle. Every day he came with a red rose saying, "Marry me, Belle, please."

As the wedding bells chimed, the beast roared in agony about the fact that Belle was marrying Adam.

Lola Whitfield (12)

Ormiston Sir Stanley Matthews Academy, Blurton

STRANGE

The sound of clocks were chiming throughout Millie's head. Then, next second, she was floating and her eyes were at the back of her head. Her friends were panicking, not knowing what to do. Then it clicked.
"What's her favourite song?"
"It's got to be here somewhere."
They all started to look through her stuff.
"I think I found it!"
They ran and turned the volume all the way up. Then they blasted the music.
"Nothing is happening!"
"We have just turned it on, you have to wait!"
Two minutes go by.
"This is not the right song!"

Skye Dawson (14)
Ormiston Sir Stanley Matthews Academy, Blurton

STRANGLED

"Mother knows best..." she claims in disbelief and utter frustration.

"No!"

"No?" she questions creeping up to me.

Panic! *Creak! Creak! Creak!*

"Stay back!" I yell.

My subconscious adrenaline pulls me in.

My hair in my hand.

"What did I do...?"

A stone-cold corpse lay before me. I quickly unwrap my hair, the marks on her neck mimicking the form of my hair. My vision goes blurry, head pounding. A small tear falls. What do I do next? I start to rummage around my room. Paint tins spilling, splatters of colour all over my dress...

Paige Smith (12)
Ormiston Sir Stanley Matthews Academy, Blurton

THE WOLF'S TALE

I was stalking the woods. I smelt something sweet. I followed the smell. I saw a small girl in a red cloak.
"Hello girl," I exclaimed excitedly.
The girl screamed fearfully. I forgot to mention that I'm a wolf. The girl attempted to escape. I grabbed her before she ran away.
"I won't eat you. I'd like to be your friend," I lied. "Where are you going all by yourself in the dangerous woods?"
"I'm going to my grandmother's cottage at the end of the woods," she replied.
I sprinted off and found the cottage, ate the grandmother and waited...

Sehar Hussain (12)
Ormiston Sir Stanley Matthews Academy, Blurton

BACK TO CHAOS

"Please Zeus, you have to help me!" pleaded Demeter crying.

"I'm sorry, but I can't help you," exclaimed Zeus.

The world began to turn back to darkness. Demeter collapsed and died. The world was slowly turning back to chaos. People began dying. The only way to restore the world was for Hades to let Persephone be free. Zeus and the other gods, apart from Hades, used their powers to stop the world from dying. However, they couldn't bring anyone back.

Five years later, Hades and Persephone were arguing when she spied a chance and killed Hades.

The world was restored.

Daniel Ward (12)
Ormiston Sir Stanley Matthews Academy, Blurton

JULIET AND HER LOVER

Two foes lived in Verona where they learned to co-exist.
Fast forward...

Juliet was in her tomb 'resting'. Paris was in tears. He
couldn't believe she'd gone. Romeo had come to see his wife
but Paris was already there... Paris knew about the family
feud. When he saw Romeo, his tears disappeared and anger
spread across his face. Paris lunged at Romeo with his
sword in his hand. He blamed Romeo for Juliet's death.
Romeo wrestled Paris. It was too late, Romeo was now
dead...

Juliet walked outside and saw Paris next to Romeo. She's
wept ever since that day.

Layla Kenny (12)
Ormiston Sir Stanley Matthews Academy, Blurton

SOMETHING WAS WRONG!

In the desolate hallways of the Republic Venator Class Destroyer, I sensed there was something evil lurking within the never-ending corridors. Suddenly, I was interrupted by an ARC trooper, alerting me that there was a leak in the cargo bay. That gave me shivers as I rushed to see the situation. However, two of my troops stopped me. *"Weird,"* I said to myself.

They were acting a little different than normal. Out of nowhere, a small tiny eel crawled out of one of the troop's noses. My hands trembled as I knew something had gone terribly wrong...

Rhys Bagnall (14)

Ormiston Sir Stanley Matthews Academy, Blurton

END IN A FLASH

The night's glow enclosed the forest. The worry of going to meet Voldemort shook me. Through the steady steps through the twigs and bushes, I saw the moonlight singing upon his head. His wand was ready. My ears shuttered with the thundering roar and my eyes evaporated with the engorging light. The curious look on my face darted towards a wizard I knew but yet a wizard I kept at heart.
"Dumbledore," I whispered.
I screamed when he pulled out of the dream by the light.
I'm awake fast but I felt strong. I was furious but it was over.

Daniel Yates (12)
Ormiston Sir Stanley Matthews Academy, Blurton

THE OCEAN

I cover most of the world and I am proud of how beautiful and colourful I am. I have wonderful creatures, both big and small and a variety of colours. I love the way the water sways when the wind blows and how everyone from around the world dives into the water to explore my hidden secrets. But if you stopped polluting and carelessly leaving your rubbish around then the loveable animals wouldn't be affected. When the oceans are full of waste, the poor creatures get tangled in plastic bags, nets, string, bottles and plastic. And they suddenly start dying.

Chloe Walker (14)
Ormiston Sir Stanley Matthews Academy, Blurton

HANSEL AND GRETEL AND THE OLD LADY

That poor woman. She told me years ago that she and her husband built that house of gingerbread and then her husband died. She cut herself off from society. That frail and ancient woman now spent her days in the house, grieving.
I was passing one day. I saw a boy and a girl devouring the gingerbread door. After breaking in, the boy began attacking the woman.
Time passed. She was forced to feed them the house, their bodies fattening. Suddenly, the girl pushed the woman into a boiling cauldron. Their cackles drowned out her screams of torment.

Finley Barker-Green (14)
Ormiston Sir Stanley Matthews Academy, Blurton

THE KING TO BE

I arose over the Serengeti lands, a sentient roar awoke me. It was the oba of the town. Animals started hurtling towards me, excitedly galloping and trotting to the right-angled rock that would showcase the crowning. I was selected to carry out the duty when I had shown great citizenship to the king. When inspecting the crown, I found marigold flowers and symbols that detailed prophecy about the kingdom. Slowly, I lifted the crown and stepped into the spotlight of the hot African sun and lowered the crown onto his head. The house of the lion was born.

Warren Brown (12)
Ormiston Sir Stanley Matthews Academy, Blurton

THE WOLF'S REVENGE

You may know me as the big bad wolf but really, I'm the good guy. Ever since my family was selfishly stolen from me, I've struggled to find food. My house is empty and it's all because of one family. Luckily for me, the youngest daughter crossed my house every morning, it was the perfect chance for revenge. Quietly, I crept out of my house and followed her until she arrived at her grandma's house. This was it!

The next morning at sunrise, I went to her grandma's house and ate her. Revenge was enough to fill me up forever.

Georgia McNair (12)

Ormiston Sir Stanley Matthews Academy, Blurton

CINDERELLA WITH A TWIST

I banged on the door.

"Let me out, you witch!"

My stepmother's footsteps slowly receded as I lost hope that I would ever see the prince again. However, I'm not certain I wanted to see him anymore. I saw his horses approaching the house and used a chair to break the door. I wanted them gone! I rushed down the stairs and slapped the prince.

"If you truly loved me you would recognise my face, not my shoe size!"

He called for me. I kicked him and his men out. I then returned to my bedroom with a sigh.

Maleeha Mahmood (13)

Ormiston Sir Stanley Matthews Academy, Blurton

ANNE'S HOLIDAY

Dear Kitty...
Currently, I'm on a train going to a summer camp called
Auschwitz. My parents are going somewhere else in Poland
for their holiday. I'm a little bit nervous as I have never left
home without my family before, especially in these times.
Luckily, I'm with my friend, Betty Lukas.
I can see the buildings of Auschwitz camp coming into view.
The train is very compact and cramped. The train is slowing
down. We're here now. The wind slaps my face like a blade
of ice. After a long journey, we have finally arrived.

Alfie Brannigan (12)
Ormiston Sir Stanley Matthews Academy, Blurton

WORLD WAR I IF GERMANY WON

It is 1937 and the German empire has officially gotten ground on two-thirds of Europe. They have taken France and the majority of eastern Europe, only western Russia is left. The UK will struggle to make a strong enough army because of the Versaille limiting their army capacity and battleship numbers but there is a rumour they are breaking it!

It is 1939 and the invasion of German-occupied France has started. I got to see British troops storm my seaside town as they forced the German troops out. Today is the start of the Second World War.

Jacob Taylor (14)
Ormiston Sir Stanley Matthews Academy, Blurton

WHAT IF PARLIAMENT WAS BLOWN UP?

You're possibly thinking how I got into this mess. Well, I'll tell you. About two weeks ago, I decided that I wanted a huge explosion. Well, what better place than Parliament, right? I hated them.

It was all over the news. Boris and fifty-seven other MPs dead. My face lit up with excitement. I heard a knock on the door. I got up and opened the door. There was a cop.

"You're coming with me," he said.

He cuffed me. I got into the car. I can't believe I didn't get away with it. I've got to escape!

Joanna Dyer (14)
Ormiston Sir Stanley Matthews Academy, Blurton

THE WATER TURNS BLACK

There would be consequences for the nature they attacked. I stumbled and tumbled down the wasteland. A sweet, oily apple slipped out of my hand. They came here and conquered, took over our homes. Many people left, wandering alone. For he was the horus, he spoke for the trees. But these cruel people brought him to his knees. This was a vast forest, it was lively, but then the Germans of the Third Reich advanced through the Ardennes. I sat there, saw them conquer and let it all be. I thought to myself, *how bad could they possibly be?*

Alfie Loveday (14)
Ormiston Sir Stanley Matthews Academy, Blurton

STRANGER THAN STRANGE

It was 1982, Thursday the 14th of January. I sat in my house staring at the walls with an ominous feeling. The faded wallpaper on the wall was torn with bricks missing. The fairy lights still hung. My mom still had hope that Will was coming home. Suddenly, the lamp flickered. Someone was here in the upside down. The fairy lights flickered. 'H' then it paused. 'E' then it paused again. 'L' and then 'P'. It spelt out 'Help'. I screamed and ran to my bedroom. I locked myself away. What was I going to do?

Ellie Fletcher (14)
Ormiston Sir Stanley Matthews Academy, Blurton

THE MONSTER AND THE THREE BEARS

We pack our bags and leave. The gloomy and dark forest and bright sun illuminate the edge.
After our adventure, we return home. From a distance, we spy the door wide open. The stench of a girl lingers in our home. Golden blonde hair spread across our carpet leading to the bedroom. The bedroom contains three beds depending on size. We open the door, ready to fend off what was in there. The room is dark with no light. A rabid beast growls in the middle bed. We call the hunter and he put the beast down. Blonde hair everywhere...

Daniel Dixon (14)

Ormiston Sir Stanley Matthews Academy, Blurton

WHAT IF THE LITTLE MERMAID COULDN'T SING?

Ariel was average. Everyone knew that there was nothing special about her except for her bright red hair. So when she begged the most notorious sea witch to make her human, she nearly had nothing to offer. Until that is, the witch told her that if she could attract a human man completely bald then she could stay human. After being shown the man, she signed away her hair and sprouted human legs. On land, she was shunned by this man. He told her that she was hideous and unloveable. She spent her days as a lonely and bald mermaid.

Lee Stanier (14)
Ormiston Sir Stanley Matthews Academy, Blurton

THE MONSTER

I was there. I was at this so-called 'mall fire' as people were calling it. But I knew that wasn't what really happened. The glass above me broke and an inky-black spider-like creature fell. It cried a war cry as if it was calling something. A girl, no older than fifteen, appeared on the balcony. She held out her hand and shot the creature back ever so slightly. It seemed to be struggling but was able to fight it. A man came from behind her, put her on his shoulder and took her to the monster's front...

Sasha Crutchley (13)
Ormiston Sir Stanley Matthews Academy, Blurton

LITTLE RED RIDING HOOD AND THE TIGER

Once upon a time, Little Red Riding Hood was skipping down an inky road. A tiger popped out of the woods and startled her.

He asked, "Where are you going?"

Little Red Riding Hood said, "To see my grandad."

He asked for one of her chocolate muffins but she said no. So he went back into the woods.

When she got to her grandad's, the tiger answered but she didn't suspect anything. When she went to the kitchen, her grandad and the tiger were talking about what they had for dinner.

Kaylub Slack (14)

Ormiston Sir Stanley Matthews Academy, Blurton

THE FORGOTTON COW

I lived a fine life with Jack. He gave me what I needed and vice-versa. Then one day it all changed. Jack came to me filled with sorrow. We walked for what felt like forever before we arrived at the market. Soon after our arrival, Jack made a deal with some old beggar for beans! I was furious. How could my worth be equal to that handful of beans? So off Jack went, leaving me behind. I couldn't believe any of this. I had been with Jack since he'd been born and he'd just abandoned me. So much for friendship!

Theodore Priest (14)
Ormiston Sir Stanley Matthews Academy, Blurton

HARRY POTTER, THE BOY WHO DIED

Harry Potter. Who is he? The boy who... died. I have been searching for twelve years now. I should introduce myself, my name is Dumbledore. Searching for what? Who? You ask. The one we do not speak of. Only once will I tell you that monster's name. Voldemort. His wand is gnarled by pure evil. He is the master of all snake art. Eyes inky as you'll ever see. Some people say he's dead. Others say he's lurking in the dark. I will soon find him, not long now, for the crime he did. He killed... Harry Potter.

Luke Meir (13)
Ormiston Sir Stanley Matthews Academy, Blurton

MY LOVE FOR HER

I saw her. I told her to run. I was in love with Katniss and I didn't want her to get hurt because of me. Butterflies and bees flew in front of my face. I had been stung by a tracker jacker. I didn't care. She was safe. I could hear Cato screaming at me. My vision was blurry and my hearing was muffled.

"Peeta, how could you? Now we will never win! She's one of the best in the arena!"

"I know," I said while watching her run off into the sunset. She was all I cared about.

Lexi Allen (12)
Ormiston Sir Stanley Matthews Academy, Blurton

THE RUNAWAY

I ran away because I couldn't bear the fact that what I did was preposterous. Mum and Dad were dead. I had no one. I guess it was just me now. I definitely had shelter. My nan's house. I mean, she wasn't in. I have one uncle that would kill me if he ever found out. Literally!

I heard a bang on the door. I approached the door and opened it. I couldn't believe it. It was him. He slowly pulled something out of his pocket. A gun.

Bang! Bang! I collapsed to the floor, unable to breathe.

Brooke Simpkin (14)
Ormiston Sir Stanley Matthews Academy, Blurton

THE FIGURE

As I looked up into the forbidding sky, my legs had a shivering feeling, making me feel unsteady. All of a sudden... *Bang!* Lightning struck my eyes. Then out came the inky, humongous figure. My heart was beating so fast and so loud. I tried to calm myself down. It just stood there gazing straight at me. My mind was stunned. My body was frozen on the spot. His legs gradually made their way towards me. My feet began to move, one foot in front of the other, faster and faster. Its deep voice chased after me...

Olive McCarthy (13)
Ormiston Sir Stanley Matthews Academy, Blurton

A TWISTED AWAKENING

With shock, I had awoken. I couldn't feel another and all I could see was a haggard-looking man, his face filled with disgust. So I left and wandered through a town, stopping to learn about the villagers, until they discovered me and called me a monster which filled me with rage. I choked the life out of the nearest one and ran away. I encountered my creator once again and pleaded with him to make others like me to which he refused and angered me once again, leading to his death. But I realised my mistake...

Kane Garvie (14)
Ormiston Sir Stanley Matthews Academy, Blurton

THE HUNGRY WOLF

I could see the little girl in red walking in the woods. I wanted to pounce on her but I couldn't. Instead, I went to her grandma's house.

When at her grandma's house, the door was left a bit open and I slipped through. She was quite small and ancient. It took one swallow to get rid of her. I quickly changed into a gown and lay in her bed.

Soon, the girl came up and saw me. She made many comments about my appearance and suspected me as fake. She knew I wasn't her grandma so I ate her.

Bradley Peake (14)
Ormiston Sir Stanley Matthews Academy, Blurton

STRANGER TWISTS

It was a charcoal and inky night, we were in Mike's basement. It was me, Lucas, Mike and Will. We were playing dungeons and dragons. We had failed to defeat the Demogorgon.

We left Mike's house.

Will said to Mike, "The Demogorgon got me."

Then he told Will to hurry up. We had a race on our bikes but Will went too far. I stopped. All of a sudden, there was a loud crash.

The next day, I found out that Will had gone missing. When it went dark, I went to search for him...

Morgan Quinn (12)

Ormiston Sir Stanley Matthews Academy, Blurton

HAUNTED SCARY CHURCH

One cold dark day I went out. I went to a haunted church. The church looked forbidding but I still went into the eerie yard. I thought I heard a cold scream from the church. All of a sudden, an unhuman woman, the colour of paper, came from nowhere and wrapped her cold hands around my neck. I quickly ran straight through the creaky door. My heart was beating through my chest.

5am and it was starting to lighten up. I was still paranoid that the woman was following me. I'm never going there again...

Chloe Dean (12)

Ormiston Sir Stanley Matthews Academy, Blurton

BLOOD BROTHERS

I sat brooding about Linda and Eddie hugging and kissing in the distance. As my day went on, I was thinking if Linda would ever cheat on me. Inch by inch, step by step, I walked towards them. It felt like hours but then I took one step and I was there. I told Eddie to give me and Linda a minute.
"Why are you with him?"
"Because he lives up here now. He asked me to marry him."
"You what? I'm going to kill him!"
"I am going to marry Eddie."

Owen Jurkowski (14)
Ormiston Sir Stanley Matthews Academy, Blurton

THE FRIAR

Why did I do it? Why did I lead two innocent teenagers to their downfall? You know the story of Romeo and Juliet? The story where they both die at the end? You know me as the friar who helped Juliet fake her death. The only reason for my wrongdoing was that I wished someone had helped me. Young and in love, I made reckless decisions. She was a beautiful woman. When her father was readying for her marriage, it was for Gustav, not me. That's why I did it. To see them get the ending I never had.

Aleeza Wahid (13)
Ormiston Sir Stanley Matthews Academy, Blurton

BEAUTY AND THE PRINCE

My father was gone. I grabbed my horse and rode and rode until I came across a huge castle. I had to explore inside. As I made my way to the iron doors, a tremendous beast rose before me. He was guarding the castle. There must have been something to treasure inside. Maybe it was the prince. The beast grabbed me and swapped my father for me. I was trapped. I heard something in the distance. Suddenly a tall handsome figure appeared in the light. It was the prince and he invited me to dinner with him!

Ella Beech (14)
Ormiston Sir Stanley Matthews Academy, Blurton

1944

The year is 1944, and the Nazis won. All Jews are dead and the world is devastated. No one opposes Hitler now. The world is destroyed but the Nazis' power in the world is falling because of a dying global economy because of an under-manned government. Poor choices have led to a resource war where people are fighting to rebuild. Everywhere is ruined. Life is near impossible. Very few humans remain in a now crippled world. The world domination plan has led to disaster. One man and army did it.

Jamie Powell (12)
Ormiston Sir Stanley Matthews Academy, Blurton

FROM BADNIK TO GOODNIK

After an onslaught of defeats from the hedgehog, Sonic, I, Doctor Eggman, have decided to turn over a new leaf, to start anew for the good of the people. From now on, I will use my machines and vast intellect to make the world, not into my empire, but into a utopia for everybody to be free. Free to enjoy the new world order and the freedom it treats them to. And as for me? Well, the world will be ready to see the brand-new Eggman and so will Sonic.
I will make the world into a paradise

Lennon Birks (14)
Ormiston Sir Stanley Matthews Academy, Blurton

AM I REALLY A VILLAIN?

You may know me from that fairy tale, you know, Tangled.
This is my story...
I stole the princess but no one knows why. That family was
the reason my real daughter was dead. I wanted revenge. I
never knew how badly behaved she was or I would never
have taken her. She makes me go miles just so she gets the
food she wants and threatens me by saying she will leave
the tower. How I want to take her back but never can
because of the guards. I wish I never took her in the first
place...

Jorja Lloyd (14)
Ormiston Sir Stanley Matthews Academy, Blurton

THE GHOSTS

Me and my mate were walking back from work and stopped by an abandoned church that had been built around 1,000 years ago. Me being me, approached the church and opened the door.

Both of our faces became grey, old and wrinkly. Two ghosts had awakened. One ghost charged at me so I evacuated immediately. The ghosts looked at us through the stained glass and suddenly disappeared.

The next day, after we finished work, we went in there again but the ghosts did not appear again.

Danny Tudor (12)
Ormiston Sir Stanley Matthews Academy, Blurton

THE BOY WHO FELL OFF A WALL

I was sitting brooding when someone fell off a wall. It was like it was a coincidence. Inch by inch he fell. I couldn't help but laugh. When I close my eyes I can see it happening. I still giggle about it now. To be honest, I don't think I should have laughed because I didn't know who it was. If I did know who it was then it would be okay to laugh.

I approached the boy because I wanted to see if he was okay. Then I realised who it was. My face dropped. It was...

Ruby Ibbs (13)

Ormiston Sir Stanley Matthews Academy, Blurton

THE FORBIDDING HOUSE

There was an unusual town where a really bad thing happened that no one talked about. I am the only person that knows. The story starts with three people. They went into a dark forest.

When they got to the end of the dark forest, there was a building... It was an abandoned house. What they didn't know was that a family died there last year on that same day. Step by step, they all walked to the forbidding door. The sound of the door opening filled the unkempt house...

Mikala Pearce (12)

Ormiston Sir Stanley Matthews Academy, Blurton

ABERFAN DISASTER

1966, I missed my chance. I was supposed to be there helping to move the mud.
I went down the next day to try and dig someone out. I couldn't find anyone to help, they were all gone. I felt so guilty and powerless. I gave my earnings to a woman who had lost her son and carried on digging. Me and another man found a child. He was breathing. I picked him up and wrapped him in a blanket and took him home. I felt less guilty but I felt like a murderer, not a miner.

Shaylie Hughes-Jones
Ormiston Sir Stanley Matthews Academy, Blurton

CAN I ESCAPE?

I ran through the woods. I suddenly felt an eerie presence. I began to run. I reached an unkempt, desolate house. No one went to the house as people said it was haunted due to the passing of a man a few weeks prior. As I hid, there was a knock on the door. The door flew open. My heart stopped. The killer had entered. I used a bin lid as a shield and a stick as a sword. I closed my eyes and ran to the door. I caught the fastest bus and left town. I never looked back.

Catherine Ayuk (12)
Ormiston Sir Stanley Matthews Academy, Blurton

ALONE AT HOME

We were getting ready, packing our bags. We were excited about going on holiday. As everyone went to bed, I saw a van right outside with two ugly men watching the house. I thought nothing of it and fell asleep.

When I woke up, the whole house was empty. I heard mysterious noises so I checked and all our furniture was missing. I went outside and was chucked in a van by two men. Then I realised they were the same men that were watching my house yesterday...

Haleem Hussain (14)
Ormiston Sir Stanley Matthews Academy, Blurton

HOW THE TABLES TURNED

One inky, desolate day, there was a forbidding gnarled kingdom. It was a Sunday evening, King Richard III was enjoying his luxurious life. Then he went to his charcoal, desolate bedroom. Unfortunately for Richard, when he least expected it, Prince Edward came into his room. When Edward walked into the room, he had chains and a pillow. He weighed Richard down, two chains on his arms and two chains on his legs. When the right time came Edward suffocated Richard.

Codie Mason (13)
Ormiston Sir Stanley Matthews Academy, Blurton

BEAUTY AND THE BEAST

I sat brooding in my castle when a shadow emerged outside my window. *Bang!* The door flew off and a woman walked in. She was called Belle. Belle rushed up to my room and said, "Beast, you are coming with me or else I will use force!"
"No!" said the beast.
Belle stabbed the beast.
"Argh!" said the beast.
"You resisted," said Belle. "Now you die!"

Maclaine Chamboko (12)
Ormiston Sir Stanley Matthews Academy, Blurton

HUMPTY-DUMPTY

A boy wearing a bright, colourful T-shirt was walking in the park and went to sit on a wall. He started to daydream as he sat on the wall. An inky, forbidding figure walked towards him. The figure got closer, inch by inch. The figure eventually sat next to him. He budged up but the figure kept moving closer and closer until he pushed him off. Then the figure ran away. He got up and he was...

Leah Didd (13)
Ormiston Sir Stanley Matthews Academy, Blurton

THE SCHOOL

In the dark abandoned building, I started going down the stairs. I heard a loud bang. I carried on and saw loads of desks. It looked like there was a class. Suddenly, there was another bang and tables flew across the room. I ran but then the door slammed, locking me in. All I could hear were nursery rhymes. Then I heard a loud siren. The police... Then I woke up.

Shay Cosgrove (14)
Ormiston Sir Stanley Matthews Academy, Blurton

MY DEAR BEATRICE

I looked down at my darling Beatrice as if she could see me and give me the reassuring smile that she always did... but nothing. She was dead and nothing could bring her back. I crouched down and held her close. What I felt brought tears to my eyes. I felt her heart beating. She was alive!

Fiza Javaid (12)
Ormiston Sir Stanley Matthews Academy, Blurton

HAMELIN'S LOSS

Lonesome children were on a wooden bridge, which tenderly curved through the town of Hamelin. The ropes trembled back and forth as the white-gowned kids followed a tune, mesmerised, sedated to the melody. The town emptied as Hamelin's only hope faded away from the premises. Yet one boy fell, and that boy was me.

It took me long enough to resuscitate. The melody was gone now, yet vague in my memory. I breathed rapidly, shaking as I realised that the Pied Piper in yellow and red robbed the town of Hamelin, vanishing from sight.

I was enraged.

Maddie Cour (15)
The British School Of Tashkent, Uzbekistan

TANGLED

Something that bothers me, is that this story will never be told correctly.

People used to like me. They spoke to me without wincing! But then Repunzel came along. I never kidnapped her, she found me and I couldn't get rid of her.

Then, as any good parent would, the royals sent out a search party for her!

Long story short, my hot neighbour came round for a romantic dinner date and saw her. He turned me in as the 'culprit' and boom! No more social life for me. And yet to this day, I still remain the villain.

Wanda Ripper (13)
The Hemel Hempstead School, Hemel Hempstead

LITTLE RED RIDING HOOD

You probably think that I had a really bad ending and the 'bad wolf' deserved to be killed, but I didn't! I never wanted to eat a granny or a little girl. You're probably confused because people have been telling you that the wolf ate Granny and got killed by a woodcutter. I'll explain...
I wanted to eat the goods the girl had in her basket so I found out where she was going. I went into Granny's house, locked her up and waited. It was going well but Granny burst out and shot me.

Fallon Makepeace (12)
The Hemel Hempstead School, Hemel Hempstead

TWISTED GOLDILOCKS AND THE BEARS

Calmly walking, I saw a house. The door was open. I went inside with my taxidermy kit. I saw porridge. I ate it. I went upstairs and got in the bed by the window.

It was 2am. The sound of footsteps was coming up the wooden steps. The door flew open. They were bears. I grabbed my taxidermy kit. Screams banged on the walls and what looked like strawberry jam was everywhere in that room.

The next day, I walked out of the house with a new stuffed bear toy to play with and a new rug and coat.

Sophia Munns (12)

The Hemel Hempstead School, Hemel Hempstead

AMONG US

"There is an imposter among us."
The words echoed around the ship. Me and the crew were in shock. An imposter in the most heavily guarded high-security chunk of metal in human history? Seemed unlikely. Some accused others, some were in denial but me and R/1253 were in horror. We trusted each other since the first day we met and knowing it could be one of us was terrifying. It didn't help that one by one they all died until it was just me, R/1253, W/478 and O/99...

Sidney Lainton (12)
The Hemel Hempstead School, Hemel Hempstead

ROBIN HOOD

Once upon a time, there lived Robin Hood. As you might think, he gave to the poor, but he was different. Instead, of giving to the poor, he kept it. Once he stole from the rich people he kept it in his secret hideout. None of his gang members knew where it was. They trusted him so much, thinking gave it to the poor, but he would steai the money for himself. He would even steal from the king himself and keep it. That's why people thought Robin Hood was good... but he wasn't.

Nana Tawiah (12)
The Hemel Hempstead School, Hemel Hempstead

THREE LITTLE PIGGIES

There I was doing my job, on what I didn't know was my last day alive. The 'big bad wolf' earning a living by checking houses to see if they were safe. My next few stops: the houses of the three little pigs.

"Um, hello? Mandatory house check-ups. Open the door please."

Nothing. I huffed, I puffed and I blew the house down.

"This is not suitable to live in! Sir...!"

He was running away! On to piggy number two then...

Violet Ripper (13)
The Hemel Hempstead School, Hemel Hempstead

THE WEIRD DAY

It was a normal day until I got a knock at the door. I was petrified because I didn't know who it was. I looked through the peephole and saw... the Gruffalo! When I looked outside to see if it was there... it was gone! But when I turned around it was right behind me. I was so scared because I didn't know what to do. I grabbed an axe and hit him on the head. Then I wasn't scared anymore! I then sat down and had a drink.

Brooke Lowe (11)
The Hemel Hempstead School, Hemel Hempstead

HAPPY BIRTHDAY

A velvet river of blood poured out of their heads, screams of the children fuelled me. I ripped open the toys and coated them in blood. Innocent, lifeless faces stared back at me. I made a pile of bodies and toys, ready for the teachers to come back. They were in for a surprise.
"Happy 7th birthday," I muttered to myself.
I grinned and skipped off. Today was a good day.

Martha Morris (13)
The Hemel Hempstead School, Hemel Hempstead

THREE LITTLE PIGS

Once upon a time, I was building my little brick house when a massive wolf blew my brother's house down. I was scared. He was walking along the bendy path and saw my house. He came up to it and tried to blow it down. He tried once and failed. He tried again and failed. My house was on the ropes here. He did it one more time and it all came tumbling and crumbling down...

Finley Clark (12)
The Hemel Hempstead School, Hemel Hempstead

PERCY JACKSON FAILS...

Percy's symbol appeared and I was instantly jealous. He was Poseidon's son. Suddenly, Poseidon's voice came from the sky and said, "Percy Jackson, you are to go on a mission to make or break the world."
Percy decided to go alone because he didn't want anyone to get hurt. I knew I had to follow him.
When Percy arrived, I saw Kronos. I instantly knew he was doomed.
"Kronos, you have to back down before the world is destroyed."
Remaining silent, Kronos turned around and pushed Percy off the mountain. I knew I had to do something...

Francis White (13)
Thomas Mills High School, Framlingham

1917

I suddenly found myself on the front line, carrying probably the most valuable item there was. The command to stop the next attack. It was a trap. The Germans were waiting. None of the men going over the top would survive. I had to move fast. The HQ on the front line wasn't far. It was a difficult run, broken rocks and stones were everywhere because of shelling. I couldn't run on the field, it was too dangerous. But then the whistle blew. It was too late. Thousands of men climbed over the top. The Germans' plan had succeeded.

Will Aryaeenia (13)
Thomas Mills High School, Framlingham

THE BUILDER OF THE PIGS

I'm a builder. I got up at seven o'clock and got ready for another day at my favourite job. The day's job was to build two houses for two of the three little pigs.
When I got there they were waiting.
"Let's get going!"
After about five hours, we had finished both houses.
Later, when I got home, I treated myself to a nice takeaway and a good night's sleep ready for tomorrow, but first, I went for a short ride on my bike to the wolf's wood den to give him both spare house keys...

Will Alexander (13)
Thomas Mills High School, Framlingham

THE WOLF'S SNOWY ADVENTURE

The wolf was getting ready. He practised his huffs and puffs and set off. Snow was falling, it was like someone shaking salt on chips. The young wolf was cold. He looked out into the snowy distance and saw the brick house. He went from a walk to a run. His little legs couldn't keep up with his mind that was set on the house.

Moments later, he arrived at the house.

"This is for boiling my dad!" he said.

Then he huffed and puffed and blew the brick house down The wolf giggled and went home.

Timmy Newson (13)

Thomas Mills High School, Framlingham

THE THREE LITTLE PIGS: THE MOTHER'S STORY

The three little pigs had a mother. She had had a harsh childhood; not much food, cold and more. As she got older, she left and built her own house. She made it out of brick and began to decorate it. Sadly, she got a divorce from her husband and gave birth, shortly after, to three piglets.
As they grew older, money became shorter so the three little pigs had to move out. The mother had to watch as her children left.
When the little pigs' houses got blown down, she sighed, "I love my kids!"

Oscar Mayhew-Frost (13)
Thomas Mills High School, Framlingham

TALL JACK AND THE SMALL GIANT!

Jack was as tall as the ceiling. The giant was as small as a scooter wheel. Jack was going to squish the teeny-weeny giant because he was trying to get the pineapple. Jack was stomping around, trying to squish the teeny giant. He kicked him up and he caught him and squeezed him to death. His face turned purple and his hands became grey before he died. Then Jack kicked down the beanstalk. It landed on the pavement. After he destroyed the beanstalk, he made a ladder with an eye scanner so no one else could get in.

Imogen Rose (13)

Thomas Mills High School, Framlingham

THE MIRROR

You don't know the story. No one does. Even I don't know the whole truth. One thing that's true is that the girl was tricked. Poor Snow White.

I am the mirror who knows everything but after she fell to the ground, the scene went dark. When the queen got back, she smiled. She didn't need to ask. She knew the plan had worked. She was the most beautiful. I am but a slave to the palace but if I have any magic left, I wish the story could have a different ending and I think, just maybe, it will.

Emily Sheen (13)
Thomas Mills High School, Framlingham

150

THREE LITTLE PIGS

There were three little pigs and a grumpy wolf. The three little pigs were trying to build their houses to get away from the grumpy wolf. They all made their houses out of bricks. The grumpy old wolf tried to blow them down but the grumpy old wolf couldn't get in. They tried to get away but the wolf knew where they went and hid. The wolf tried to break it down and tried to find a way to break into the pig's houses. He dug a hole in the house but the pigs were not there! Whoops!

Lauren Tysoe (12)
Thomas Mills High School, Framlingham

THE ARABIAN NIGHT

I was getting married in two days. My father was making me as I was the heir. I went out to my tiger, Ruby. She always helped me. Suddenly, I decided to run away. I saw a man. He was running away from the police. I was spotted then I got grabbed by him. He told me to be quiet. He tried taking me home but I refused so he took me to his house. He really wanted me to go back as it was getting dark. Then we got on the carpet and we rode into the beautiful sunset.

Megan Berry (12)
Thomas Mills High School, Framlingham